For my sister Julie, who just arrived one day! D.B.
For my great nephew and great niece, Jack and Stella, with love. T.F.

First published in 2012 by Hodder Children's Books

Text copyright © David Bedford 2012
Illustration copyright © Tor Freeman 2012

Hodder Children's Books, 338 Euston Road, London, NW1 3BH
Hodder Children's Books Australia, Level 17/207 Kent Street, Sydney, NSW 2000

A catalogue record of this book is available from the British Library.

ISBN 978 1 444 90352 2

Printed in China

Hodder Children's Books is a division of Hachette Children's Books,
an Hachette UK Company

www.hachette.co.uk

BABIES DON'T BITE

DAVID BEDFORD AND TOR FREEMAN

Hodder Children's Books

A division of Hachette Children's Books

One morning,

Hegley went trotting down
to the farmyard with some
exciting news.

'My mum's having a baby!' said Hegley.

He kicked his back legs high in the air and bounced
about to celebrate.

To Hegley's surprise, his friends did not look happy.

Pigmeal oinked gloomily, 'My mum's having a baby, too.'

'So is my mum,' baaed Sheeply.

'So is my mum,' mooed Cowhide.

'Babies are nothing to bounce about,' said Pigmeal. 'I've heard that babies pull tails.'

Hegley stopped bouncing. 'Really?' he said. 'I never knew babies pulled tails! I'll go and tell my mum.'

But on his way home...

Hegley found **ten** baby rabbits with tickly, twitchy noses,

nine baby guinea pigs with smiley faces,

and **eight** baby kittens
with bright, shiny eyes.

'Mum, Pigmeal told me that babies
pull tails but they don't!' said Hegley.
'Babies are fab!'
And Hegley now had even
more exciting news to tell
his friends.

'My mum's got a big tummy!' said Hegley, skipping to celebrate.
'The baby is growing!'

Sheeply baaed sadly, 'My mum's got a big tummy, too.'
'So has my mum,' oinked Pigmeal.
'So has my mum,' mooed Cowhide.

'Babies are nothing to skip about,' said Sheeply.
'I've heard that babies bite.'

Hegley stopped skipping. 'Really?' he said.
'I'll go and tell my mum.' But on his way home...

Hegley saw **seven** baby swans
with fluffy, soft feathers,

six baby puppies, wanting
to be friends,

and **five** baby chicks,
playing hide-and-seek!

'Mum, Sheeply told me that babies
bite but they don't!' said Hegley.
'Babies are fab!'
And Hegley now had the most
exciting news for his friends
so far.

'My mum's getting ready,' neighed Hegley, jumping in the air to celebrate. 'The baby will be here very soon!'

Cowhide mooed miserably, 'My mum's getting ready, too.'

'So is my mum,' oinked Pigmeal.

'So is my mum,' baaed Sheeply.

'Babies are nothing to jump about,' said Cowhide. 'I've heard that babies don't like big brothers and sisters.'

Hegley stopped jumping. 'Really?' he said.
'I'll go and tell my mum.' But on his way home...

Hegley played with **four** wriggly-wiggly piglets,

three shivery-shaky lambs,

and **two** wibbly-wobbly calves.

But Hegley had no more time to play.
He raced straight home to find...

One
baby sister.

Hegley felt big and shy.
But he knew all about babies now, and so...

...very gently, Hegley nuzzled his sister's nose.
And very gently, his sister nuzzled him back.

She was just the way Hegley had hoped a baby sister would be.
He couldn't wait to tell his friends.

Hegley bounced and skipped and jumped down to the farmyard with his sister.

But when he found Pigmeal, Sheeply and Cowhide, they already knew the best thing of all about babies...

...babies are fab and they **love** their big brothers and sisters to bits!